Eerie English

Alison Head

In a cave far away, lives a powerful wizard named Whimstaff. He spends his days finding the answers to ancient English problems and has parchments filled with wonderful words. In this book, Whimstaff shares his knowledge to help you to master the art of English.

Whimstaff has a goblin assistant named Pointy, who is very clever. Pointy helps Whimstaff perfect his spells and gets annoyed with the laziness of Mugly and Bugly, his fat pet frogs. They spend most of their time eating and sleeping and do as little work as possible.

Pointy also helps Whimstaff look after Miss Snufflebeam, a young dragon who is rather clumsy and often loses Whimstaff's words!

Wizard Whimstaff and his friends are very happy solving English problems. Join them on a magical quest to win the Trophy of English Wizardry!

Contents

Perfect Plurals

I'm Wizard Whimstaff and I'm here to teach you how to write about more than one person or thing! The trick is choosing the correct word ending to make objects plural, like s, es or ie. You need to learn the rules and the important exceptions.

spider**s**   fox**es**   bab**ies**

Allakazan!

Task 1 Most plural nouns end with **s**, but if they have a buzzing sound at the end, made by **s**, **x**, **ch** or **sh**, they end in **es**. Can you underline the magic words below which add **es** to make the plural? Hey Presto!

a cave	**b** hex	**c** spell	**d** box	**e** bench
f cat	**g** wish	**h** hiss	**i** witch	**j** wizard

Task 2 Nouns that end in a consonant followed by **y**, end in **ies** in the plural. Can you turn the singular words in brackets into plurals to complete these sentences?

a Miss Snufflebeam played with the (toy) _____.

b Pointy carried the (tray) _____ of food.

c Mugly and Bugly ate two green (jelly) _____.

d Wizard Whimstaff heard the owl's (cry) _____.

e Pointy dropped the bunch of (key) _____.

f Mugly and Bugly love going to (party) _____.

g Miss Snufflebeam played with the (puppy) _____.

h Wizard Whimstaff had no (worry) _____.

> Nouns that end in a vowel, then **y**, just need **s** to become plural: day**s**.

2

Task 3
Some words don't need their spelling changed to make the plural, as either there is no singular version, or the word stays the same whether it is singular or plural. Can you colour in the cloud with the word that stays the same? Just do the best you can.

a book   bag   salmon   tree   d spoon   brick   scissors   apple

b spectacles   dress   hat   coat   e shoe   shorts   boat   banana

c house   deer   car   chair   f goat   cave   buffalo   road

Task 4
These words don't follow the rules at all and change completely in the plural. Can you spot the correct plural for the words in red and draw a circle around it? Abracadabra!

a	mouse	mouses	mice	mices
b	child	childes	childs	children
c	man	men	mans	mens
d	woman	womans	women	womens
e	die	dice	dies	dices
f	person	perses	people	persona

Sorcerer's Skill Check

Can you work your magic and write in the plural for these nouns?

a baby _____

b house _____

c girl _____

d bus _____

e dish _____

f lolly _____

g mackerel _____

h woman _____

Good work brainbox! Time to stick your first silver shield on the trophy at the back of the book!

Vexing Vowels

I'm Pointy, sWizard Whimstaff's assistant and I'm here to help you become an English whizz! First, you must learn about words that end with vowels other than e, such as a, i, o and u.

banan<u>a</u>   sk<u>i</u>   banj<u>o</u>   em<u>u</u>

It is important to look at endings so you know how to turn singular words into plural words. Super!

Task 1 To get you started, can you write in the missing vowels in these words? Practice makes perfect!

a broccol

b kiw

c polk

d sof

e iglo

f tang

g em

h comm

i pizz

j cell

k potat

l pian

Task 2 Words that end in **o** can be tricky because some of them add an e in the plural. Can you decide which ending these words will have?

radio   solo   volcano   echo   cargo   zoo   piano   domino

s

es

Task 3
Can you write the plural form of these words? Watch out though, some of them keep the same spelling! Use a dictionary to help you.

a ski _____

b sauna _____

c fungus _____

d yo-yo _____

e patio _____

f tattoo _____

g sheep _____

h spaghetti _____

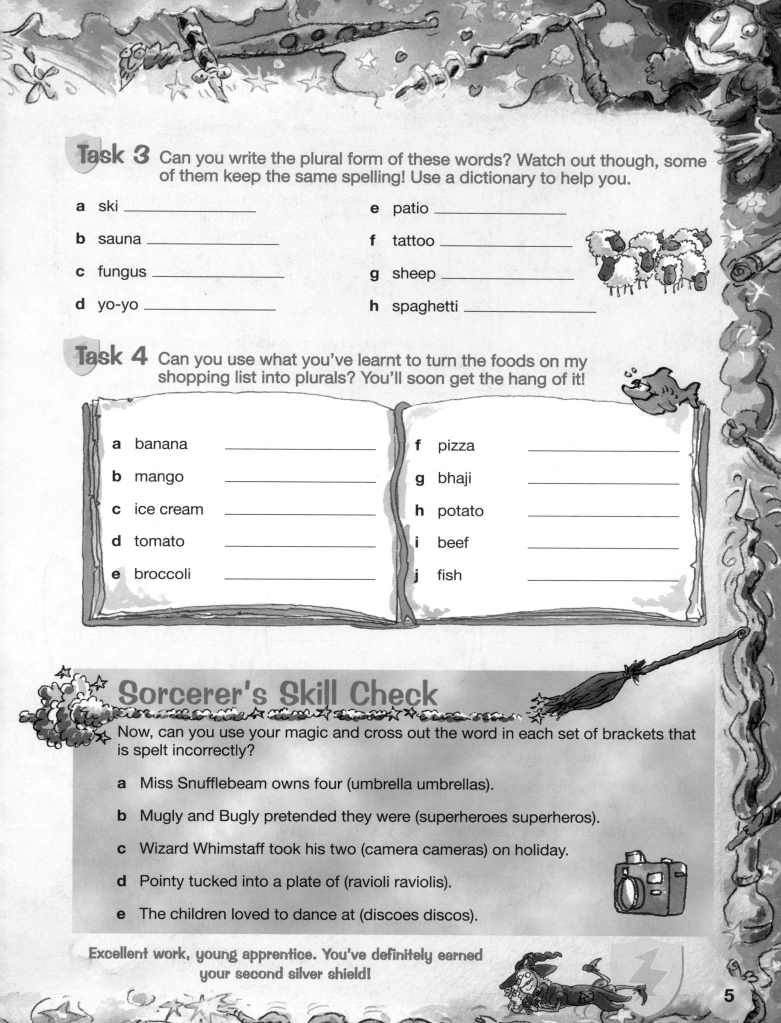

Task 4
Can you use what you've learnt to turn the foods on my shopping list into plurals? You'll soon get the hang of it!

a banana _____

b mango _____

c ice cream _____

d tomato _____

e broccoli _____

f pizza _____

g bhaji _____

h potato _____

i beef _____

j fish _____

Sorcerer's Skill Check

Now, can you use your magic and cross out the word in each set of brackets that is spelt incorrectly?

a Miss Snufflebeam owns four (umbrella umbrellas).

b Mugly and Bugly pretended they were (superheroes superheros).

c Wizard Whimstaff took his two (camera cameras) on holiday.

d Pointy tucked into a plate of (ravioli raviolis).

e The children loved to dance at (discoes discos).

Excellent work, young apprentice. You've definitely earned your second silver shield!

Sizzling Synonyms

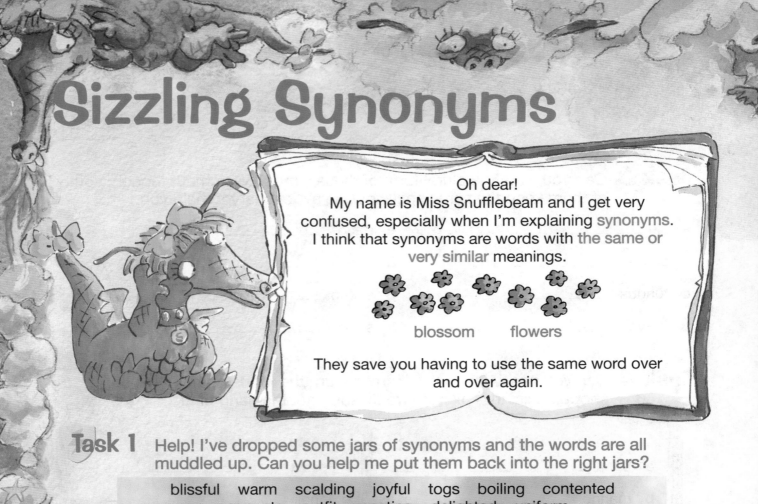

Oh dear!
My name is Miss Snufflebeam and I get very confused, especially when I'm explaining synonyms. I think that synonyms are words with the same or very similar meanings.

blossom   flowers

They save you having to use the same word over and over again.

Task 1 Help! I've dropped some jars of synonyms and the words are all muddled up. Can you help me put them back into the right jars?

blissful   warm   scalding   joyful   togs   boiling   contented
garments   outfit   roasting   delighted   uniform

happy

hot

clothing

Task 2 Often, synonyms don't have exactly the same meaning, so you have to take care when choosing the one that fits best. Can you colour in the sweet with the synonym that is the best match for the word in red?

a Wizard Whimstaff was cross when Mugly and Bugly ate all the cakes.

angry   frustrated   disheartened

b Pointy ran fast to the cave.

busily   quickly   abruptly

c Mugly and Bugly made a real noise with their croaking.

babble   blare   row

d Miss Snufflebeam tried to blow smoke rings.

puff   blast   pant

e Mugly and Bugly devoured their dinner.

consumed   gobbled   nibbled

f Wizard Whimstaff grabbed the spell book.

caught   plucked   seized

Task 3 Oh dear! I'm supposed to find synonyms for these words. Can you help?

a clever _____   d sea _____   g breeze _____

b broken _____   e magical _____   h blossom _____

c quiet _____   f tired _____   i home _____

Task 4 My head hurts! I wish I was as quick as you! Can you write a sentence using each of these synonyms?

a protect _____   b guard _____

_____   _____

c preserve _____   d keep _____

_____   _____

Sorcerer's Skill Check

There's just one more exercise I need your help with. Wizard Whimstaff likes to keep his collections of magical words neat and tidy. Can you match up the pairs of synonyms by drawing a line between them?

magic	glad
bewitched	sorcery
magician	conjurer
happy	bog
cave	spooky
creepy	spellbound
swamp	grotto

Super work! Add another silver shield to your trophy.

Spooky Speech

It's time to learn about direct and reported speech, and how to use them in your writing.

Direct speech is an actual quote from the person speaking and uses speech marks.

Croak

"Croak," said Mugly and Bugly.

Reported speech describes what someone said, but not using their exact words. It's not a quote, so you don't need to use speech marks.

I am going for a walk

Miss Snufflebeam said she was going for a walk.

Task 1

Can you read these sentences and decide whether they include direct or reported speech? Then wave your wand and tick the correct star at the end of each sentence.

		direct speech	reported speech
a	"I'm going out," said Pointy.	☆	☆
b	"Slurp!" said Mugly.	☆	☆
c	Wizard Whimstaff said the spell would work.	☆	☆
d	Miss Snufflebeam said, "My head hurts!"	☆	☆
e	Bugly said he would eat all the bugs.	☆	☆
f	Pointy asked why the spell didn't work.	☆	☆

Task 2

Now let's practise the punctuation you need when you write direct speech. Can you add in the speech marks? Remember, practice makes perfect!

a Wizard Whimstaff said, Let's clean up the cave.

b Pointy asked, Where are Mugly and Bugly?

c Time to go! called out Miss Snufflebeam.

d Grub's up! yelled Mugly and Bugly.

e Miss Snufflebeam said, This is very confusing!

Punctuation marks, like exclamation and question marks, go inside the speech marks. So do full stops and commas.

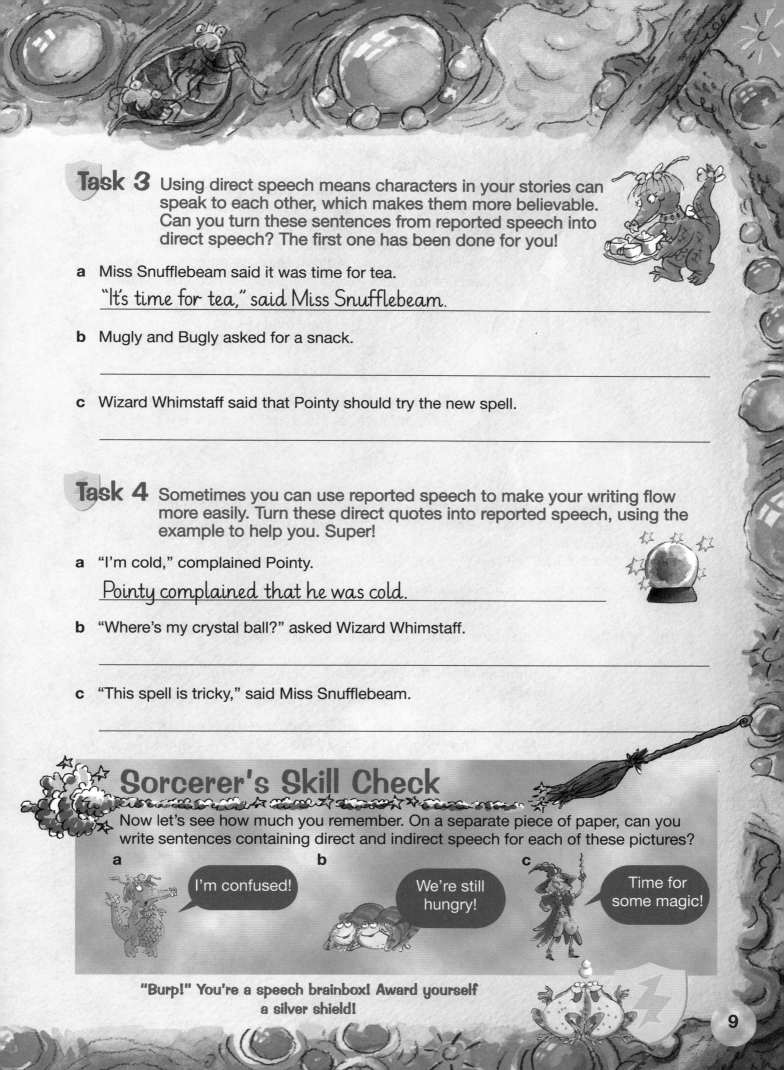

Task 3 Using direct speech means characters in your stories can speak to each other, which makes them more believable. Can you turn these sentences from reported speech into direct speech? The first one has been done for you!

a Miss Snufflebeam said it was time for tea.

"It's time for tea," said Miss Snufflebeam.

b Mugly and Bugly asked for a snack.

_____

c Wizard Whimstaff said that Pointy should try the new spell.

_____

Task 4 Sometimes you can use reported speech to make your writing flow more easily. Turn these direct quotes into reported speech, using the example to help you. Super!

a "I'm cold," complained Pointy.

Pointy complained that he was cold.

b "Where's my crystal ball?" asked Wizard Whimstaff.

_____

c "This spell is tricky," said Miss Snufflebeam.

_____

Sorcerer's Skill Check

Now let's see how much you remember. On a separate piece of paper, can you write sentences containing direct and indirect speech for each of these pictures?

a I'm confused!

b We're still hungry!

c Time for some magic!

"Burp!" You're a speech brainbox! Award yourself a silver shield!

9

Stupendous Stories

It's time to brush up your story-writing skills. The secret to writing stories lies in the preparation. If you write a good plan and develop strong characters and settings, then you won't go wrong. You can also use adjectives and similes to bring your characters and settings to life.

A simile says that something is like something else:

The monster's eyes were as black as the night.

The boat was tossed on the sea like a cork.

Task 1   I want you to plan writing a story about two friends who fight a fierce dragon to save their village. To start with, think about how you want the story to go, using the plan below to help you. Then jot down your ideas on a separate piece of paper.

Introduction:	Characters *(names, appearance, personality)*
	Setting *(where is it, what does it look like, time of day, season, weather)*
Build-up:	*What happens to your characters before the climax of the story? Where will the action take place? How do they get there? How are your characters feeling before the action takes place?*
Conflict:	*What problem does your character (or characters) meet in the story? How do your characters feel? What do they say and do?*
Climax:	*What happens as a result? How do your characters feel about it?*
Resolution:	*What changes for the characters as a result of what has happened?*

The end

Task 2
Now let's practise developing really strong characters. Try drawing lines to match up the characters with the right adjectives and adverbs. There are three for each character. Abracadabra!

a   a small, friendly troll

b   a bad-tempered professor

c   a fierce sea-monster

is grumpy

trots happily

grumbles angrily

thrashes wildly

is huge

giggles

is cheerful

roars furiously

complains loudly

Task 3
Similes are great for livening up your settings and characters. Can you make up similes for these and weave them into your story? Hey presto!

a   a dark cave _____

b   a high mountain _____

c   a spooky forest _____

d   a thunderstorm _____

e   a tiny house _____

Task 4
Time to start writing! Find a separate piece of paper and off you go! Follow your plan from Task 1 and link your ideas together, so your story flows smoothly. Try to include adjectives, adverbs and similes to breathe life into your characters and settings.

Sorcerer's Skill Check

For your last magical task, I want you to imagine that a man has moved in next door and he is the meanest, grumpiest person you have ever met. What does he look like? Using a separate piece of paper, draw a picture of how you think he'd look, then use adjectives, adverbs and similes to write a description.

Super! Your characters and settings are really lifelike! Add another silver shield to your trophy!

Creepy Consonants

My head hurts!
Consonants have their own special spelling patterns. There are spelling rules for words beginning with a soft c, like circus, or ending with suffixes such as ed, ing, er or ful, like beautiful.

circus

beautiful

Can you help me learn the rules?

Task 1 I'm confused! I think that if you want to add **full** to the end of a word like **boast**, you have to spell it **ful**. Can you complete these word sums for me? I've done the first one to show you how.

If the word you're adding **full** to ends in **y**, like beauty, you have to change the **y** to **i** first: beautiful.

a { thank } + { full } = _thankful_   e { play } + { full } = _____

b { mercy } + { full } = _____   f { fancy } + { full } = _____

c { shame } + { full } = _____   g { scorn } + { full } = _____

d { dread } + { full } = _____   h { plenty } + { full } = _____

Task 2 Help! Read these words out loud and circle the ones that start with the soft **c** sound. If you look at the letter after the **c** in each word, you will learn the soft **c** rule!

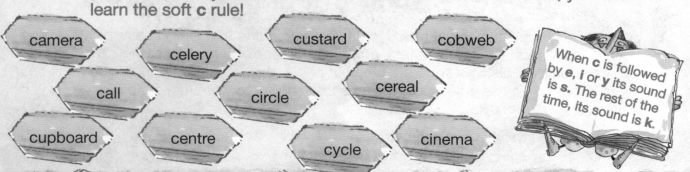

camera   celery   custard   cobweb

call   circle   cereal

cupboard   centre   cycle   cinema

When c is followed by e, i or y its sound is s. The rest of the time, its sound is k.

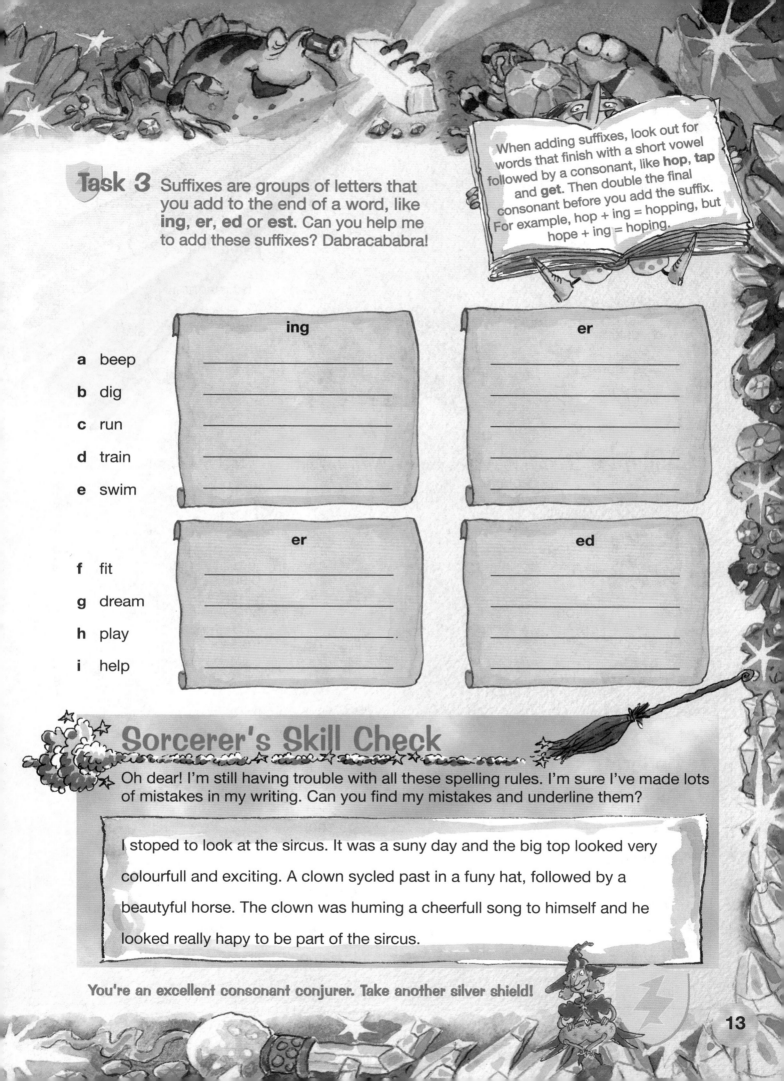

Task 3 Suffixes are groups of letters that you add to the end of a word, like **ing, er, ed** or **est**. Can you help me to add these suffixes? Dabracababra!

> When adding suffixes, look out for words that finish with a short vowel followed by a consonant, like **hop**, **tap** and **get**. Then double the final consonant before you add the suffix. For example, hop + ing = hopping, but hope + ing = hoping.

ing

a beep

b dig

c run

d train

e swim

er

er

f fit

g dream

h play

i help

ed

Sorcerer's Skill Check

Oh dear! I'm still having trouble with all these spelling rules. I'm sure I've made lots of mistakes in my writing. Can you find my mistakes and underline them?

I stoped to look at the sircus. It was a suny day and the big top looked very colourfull and exciting. A clown sycled past in a funy hat, followed by a beautyful horse. The clown was huming a cheerfull song to himself and he looked really hapy to be part of the sircus.

You're an excellent consonant conjurer. Take another silver shield!

Apprentice Wizard Challenge 1

Challenge 1

Magic bubbles from the cauldron have covered up the ends of these words. Can you write in the missing vowel to complete each word?

a bing

b past

c sk

d eskim

e camer

f pog

g pand

h magnoli

i sals

j hell

k are

Challenge 2

Can you fill the gaps in Wizard Whimstaff's table of singulars and plurals?

Singular	Plural
dog	
	dishes
box	
	losses
lady	
	babies

Challenge 3

Can you think of synonyms for these words?

a laugh _____

b frightened _____

c tired _____

d luggage _____

e parcel _____

f look _____

g shop _____

h road _____

i run _____

j tale _____

k lamp _____

l seat _____

Challenge 4
Can you turn this reported speech into direct speech? Remember to use speech marks!

a Wizard Whimstaff said he was going for a walk.

_____

b Miss Snufflebeam asked Pointy where the potion was.

_____

c Mugly and Bugly said they were hungry.

_____

d Pointy told Wizard Whimstaff the spell had worked.

_____

Challenge 5
These are all sections from a story plan. Can you rewrite them in the correct order?

climax   resolution   introduction   conflict   build-up

_____

_____

Challenge 6
These sentences have broken all the spelling rules for words which begin or end in consonants. Underline the spelling mistakes, then write the correct spelling in the box at the end of each sentence.

a Miss Snufflebeam felt bashfull.

b Pointy was gratefull for the present.

c Wizard Whimstaff stood in the magic sircle.

d Pointy loves to sycle down hills.

Count how many challenges you got right and put stars on the test tube to show your score. Then have a silver shield for your trophy!

6

5

4

3

2

1

Challenge Score

Loopy Letter Strings

Now pay close attention, young apprentice. Sometimes the same groups or strings of letters appear together in words, but are pronounced differently.

shi**el**d

p**ie**

When you read out loud, or if you need to find words that rhyme, it's important to know how to pronounce the letter strings you find in words.

Task 1 Allakazan! Can you sort these groups of words out according to the sounds made by the letter strings in red? Say them out loud and listen to how they are pronounced. Then colour the boxes with the longer sounding vowels in blue and the short sounding ones in red.

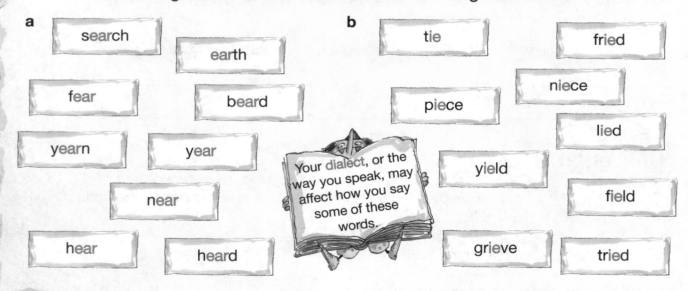

a

search

earth

fear

beard

yearn

year

near

hear

heard

Your dialect, or the way you speak, may affect how you say some of these words.

b

tie

fried

niece

piece

lied

yield

field

grieve

tried

Task 2 Read the word in the cloud, then circle the words in which the letter string is pronounced the same way. Then underline the letter that affects the way the string is pronounced.

a

w**eight**

right light freight
eight fright

b

l**ear**n

earn near yearn
dear fear

c

h**oo**k

look loot boot
rook hoot

16

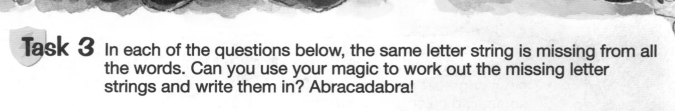

Task 3 In each of the questions below, the same letter string is missing from all the words. Can you use your magic to work out the missing letter strings and write them in? Abracadabra!

a p _ _ _   f l _ _ _   n e i g h b _ _ _ _   c o l _ _ _

b b r _ _ _ _   t _ _ _ _   h e _ _ _ _   d e l _ _ _ _

c p _ _ _   c l _ _ _   s _ _ _ c h   h _ _ _ d

d t _ _   t h _ _ v e s   w o r r _ _ d   l _ _ d

Task 4 Can you draw lines to match up the pairs of words that end with the same letter string and also rhyme?

a right   **b** fear   **c** wear   **d** niece   **e** favour   **f** pour   **g** soot   **h** bare

flavour   tight   piece   year   your   bear   scare   foot

Sorcerer's Skill Check

See how many different words you can make with the letter strings below. Remember, the letter string can appear anywhere in the word and won't sound the same every time. The first two words are done for you each time, but there are lots more to find.

a	**ai**	pair	straight
b	**ea**	bread	mean
c	**ou**	couch	sought
d	**oo**	noodle	cook
e	**ight**	weight	rightful
f	**ei**	deceive	sleigh

That made my head hurt! Have another silver shield!

Pesky Pronouns

Possessive pronouns are words you can use instead of a noun or proper noun, to show that something belongs to someone or something. Possessive pronouns like my, ours, his, theirs and yours save you having to use the same noun or name over and over again. You'll soon get the hang of it!

Miss Snufflebeam picked up <u>her</u> hat.
She knew it was <u>hers</u>!

Task 1 Mugly and Bugly have eaten some of my possessive pronouns. Can you write the missing pronouns back in? Practice makes perfect!

a	**I**	That's ___my___ book.	That book is ___mine___.
b	**you**	That's _____ book.	That book is _____.
c	**he**	That's _____ book.	That book is _____.
d	**she**	That's _____ book.	That book is _____.
e	**it**	That's _____ book.	That book is _____.

Task 2 Let's see if you can spot possessive pronouns at work. Can you work your magic and circle the possessive pronouns in these sentences?

a The cat licked its paws.

b Miss Snufflebeam loves playing. Her favourite game is blowing puffs of smoke.

c Mugly and Bugly ate their snack quickly and then they asked for more.

d Wizard Whimstaff realised the hat was his.

e If something is mine, you should ask before you borrow it.

Task 3 Now you know what pronouns look like, let's see if you can use them in these sentences. Just choose the correct possessive pronoun to fill each space.

a The boy picked up _____his_____ bag.

b They managed to catch _____ bus.

c "I like your hat. Is this one _____ too?"

d The spider hid in _____ web.

e The bats flew back to _____ cave.

f "Get off! That's _____!" yelled the boys.

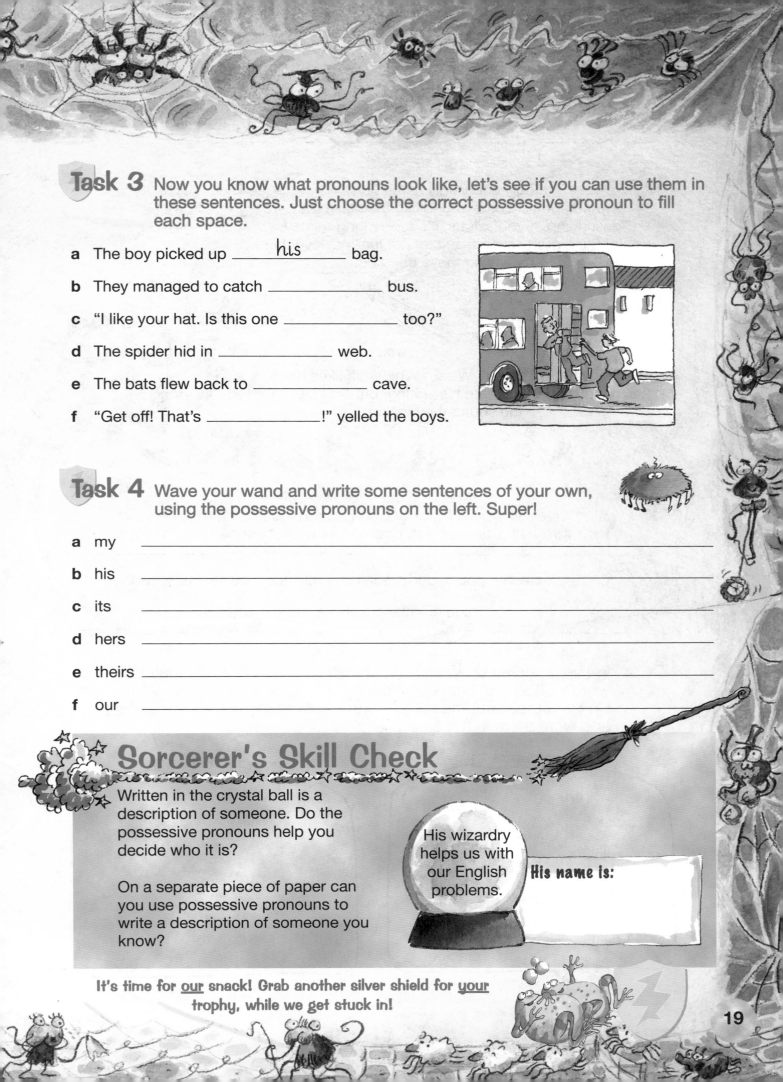

Task 4 Wave your wand and write some sentences of your own, using the possessive pronouns on the left. Super!

a my _____

b his _____

c its _____

d hers _____

e theirs _____

f our _____

Sorcerer's Skill Check

Written in the crystal ball is a description of someone. Do the possessive pronouns help you decide who it is?

On a separate piece of paper can you use possessive pronouns to write a description of someone you know?

His wizardry helps us with our English problems.

His name is:

It's time for <u>our</u> snack! Grab another silver shield for <u>your</u> trophy, while we get stuck in!

19

Odious Onomatopoeias

Mugly and Bugly here! Slurp!
Onomatopoeic words sound like the noise they are describing. If you ask us, it's a very long name for something pretty simple and lots of fun. We love them. Try saying these out loud:

pop   whizz

See what we mean? Wizard Whimstaff likes them because they liven up his writing, but we just like the sound they make!

Task 1 Slurp! Not all words that describe sounds are onomatopoeic. While we tuck into a snack, can you circle the onomatopoeic words in this lot?

crash   pop   loud   screech   silence   noise   fizz   yell

squirt   clang   shout   drip   whoosh

Task 2 We've muddled up Wizard Whimstaff's collection of onomatopoeic words. This jar should only hold the words he collected at our frog pond. Can you cross out the sounds you wouldn't expect to hear at the pond and write them in the empty jar next to it?

crunch
croak   hiss
          splosh
splash   slurp
plop   screech   drip
            dribble
crinkle
            crackle

Task 3
Burp! It's hard-going watching you work! We bet you can't pick the right words from the cauldron to fill the gaps in these sentences!

a The cauldron _____.

b The fireworks went off with a _____.

c Mugly and Bugly _____ the biscuits.

d The water _____ from the leaky tap.

e _____ went the doorbell.

> bubbled   bang
> ding dong
> trickled
> munched

Task 4
Now for the fun bit! Can you make up your own onomatopoeias to describe these sounds? See how many different ones you can come up with!

a glass breaking _____

b balloon bursting _____

c chips frying _____

d waves breaking on a beach _____

e wind in the trees _____

Sorcerer's Skill Check

Grub's up! Time for another bite to eat while you do one last task. Write a sentence using each of these onomatopoeias. Thinking about what might make each sound should give you some ideas.

a whoosh _____

b wham _____

c whine _____

d clang _____

You're a whizz at onomatopoeia! Time to stick another silver shield on your trophy!

Splendid Suffixes

Oh dear! I always get in such a muddle with suffixes. A suffix is a group of letters you add to the end of a word to change its meaning: ly, able, ing, ful, like, ic and worthy are all suffixes.

running   heroic

Sometimes you need to change the spelling of the word before you can add the suffix. Can you help me learn Pointy's magic rules?

Task 1
Help! Look at Pointy's rule and use it on the words in brackets to complete these sentences.

a The frog was (leap) _____ into the pond.

b Miss Snufflebeam was (bake) _____ a cake.

c Pointy was (break) _____ the eggs into a bowl.

d Mugly and Bugly were (hope) _____ for a snack.

e Pointy was (teach) _____ Miss Snufflebeam a new spell.

f Wizard Whimstaff was (tame) _____ a spider.

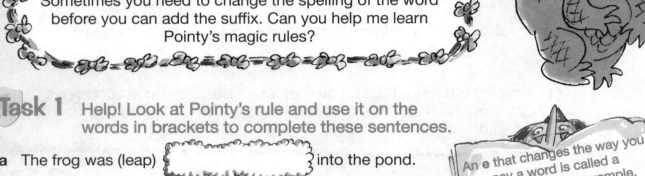

An **e** that changes the way you say a word is called a **modifying e**. For example, tap + e = tape. Words like take, slope and type lose their **e** when you add **ing**. For example, tape + ing = taping.

Task 2
Look at Pointy's second rule to do these word sums. Cabracadada!

If you want to add a suffix that begins with a consonant like **ly, worthy** or **ful** (see page 12), you leave the **e** where it is.

a tune + ful = _____   **e** live + ly = _____

b care + less = _____   **f** save + ed = _____

c blame + worthy = _____   **g** nice + est = _____

d note + able = _____   **h** brave + ly = _____

Task 3 Oh dear! Wizard Whimstaff wants me to gather some words for a new spell! Can you fill in the book below using Pointy's third rule?

> If a word ends in **y** with a consonant in front of it, you have to change the **y** to **i** before you can add most suffixes. But, if you want to add **ly** or **ing**, you can leave the **y**.

	ness		**er**
a	happy		
b	lovely		
c	heavy		
d	creepy		
e	empty		
	ing		**ed**
f	carry		
g	try		
h	reply		
i	dry		
j	deny		

Sorcerer's Skill Check

Finally, I've tried to use the spelling rules for suffixes in these sentences. Can you see if I've made any mistakes? If you find any, circle them and write the correct spelling at the end of the sentence.

a I look away (shily) when I meet strangers. ___shyly___

b Mugly and Bugly always eat so greedyly. _____

c The mouse scurryed into its hole. _____

d Wizard Whimstaff is the brainyest person I know. _____

e Pointy fryed some eggs for breakfast. _____

Croak! Watching you working has made us tired. Grab another silver shield while we grab forty winks!

23

Amazing Articles

Writing articles for newspapers is easy when you know how. Just remember to get to the point right away and include all the really important information first to grab your reader's attention. It's important to separate the main story from all the other information that may be very interesting, but isn't crucial to the story. The rest is easy. Just follow these steps. Super!

Task 1 Can you squeeze all the important information from this story into one sentence? You'll soon get the hang of it.

Last Tuesday, Wizard's convention. Magic Circle tried out new growing spell. Spell went wrong because one of the ingredients was missing. Leader of Magic Circle shrunk to size of mouse. New spell being brewed to undo the magic. Next convention scheduled for December.

Write your sentence here:

_____

_____

_____

_____

_____

_____

Task 2 Now look at the story again and answer these questions. This gives you the important information you need to write your story.

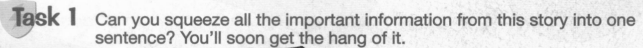

a What has happened? _____

b Where did it happen? _____

c Why did it happen? _____

d Who was involved? _____

e When did it happen? _____

Task 3 Now look at the sentences below. Can you use my tips to tick the ones which would work well in a newspaper article? Put a cross in the box after the ones that wouldn't work.

Pointy's Article Tips
- Make your language formal, not chatty.
- Use the past tense if you are writing about something that has already happened.
- It's best to stick to the facts, rather than giving your own opinion.
- If you want to quote someone, you need to say who they are.

a It was sort of dark, really. ☐

It was a dark night. ☐

b The Wizard's convention was held last week. It was a great success. ☐

The Wizard's convention will be held last week. It's a great success. ☐

c The troll denied stealing the wand. The policeman said he did. ☐

The troll denies stealing the wand, but he probably did. ☐

d The flood swept through the town. "Everything was soaked." The rain finally stopped on Thursday. ☐

The flood swept through the town. The mayor explained: "Everything was soaked." The rain finally stopped on Thursday. ☐

Task 4 Super! I think you're well prepared to write your own article about the Wizard's convention now, using my article tips above. Do this on a separate piece of paper. Remember to start with your answer to **a** from Task 2, then include the other important information, before finishing off with any background information you think your reader may be interested in.

Sorcerer's Skill Check

Practice makes perfect! Looking at how other people write newspaper articles will help you to improve your technique. Collect some stories from real newspapers and underline the answers to these questions:

What has happened?   Where did it happen?   Why did it happen?
Who was involved?   When did it happen?

Allakazan! First class reporting! Collect another silver shield!

Perplexing Poems

I'm learning to write poems.
Wizard Whimstaff says they are really simple
to write, but very effective. You just have to
choose a theme, then list different ways of
describing it. Adjectives are important.

red is a
poppy

red is a
ladybird

strawberry
red

Can you help me practise?

Task 1   I've chosen green as the theme for this poem, but I'm in a muddle with the adjectives. Can you pick the right adjective from the box to fill each gap?

first   hopping   rolling   crispy   sparkling   well-clipped   juicy   munching

Green is a _____ apple,   A _____ emerald,

The _____ hills,   The _____ leaf of spring,

A _____ caterpillar,   And a _____ lawn.

A _____ lettuce,   Green is the colour of nature.

A _____ frog,

Task 2   Oh dear! I'm in a muddle with these poems. The lines from the end of my poem about the rain have got muddled up with other weather poems. Can you pick out the lines about the rain to complete my poem?

Rain splashes down;
Washing pavements,
Spattering leaves,

_____

_____

_____

_____

swelling puddles
tearing at the trees
baking the earth
whipping up the dry leaves
drumming on umbrellas
gushing in gutters
rattling on the roof
chasing the clouds
soaking the roots of plants

Task 3 Help! I'm writing a poem about being excited but I've got stuck! Can you finish it for me? Think about things that you get excited about. The lines don't need to rhyme, but rhythm is important. Read it to yourself as you work, to make sure it sounds good.

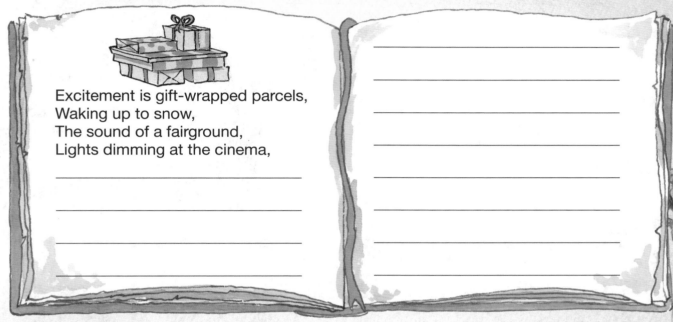

Excitement is gift-wrapped parcels,
Waking up to snow,
The sound of a fairground,
Lights dimming at the cinema,

_____

_____

_____

Task 4 My head hurts, but you're really good at this! Can you show me again? Choose one of these colours as the theme for a poem, then write it on a separate piece of paper.

red   white   yellow

Sorcerer's Skill Check

I like collecting the first lines of poems but I've dropped my collection and they are all mixed up. Can you draw lines to match them up again?

a Friendship is

b Blue is

c Autumn is

d Foods I love are

e Seaside holidays are

f A trip to the zoo means

chocolate and cake.

russet leaves rustling.

buckets and spades.

zebra stripes.

a summer sky.

sharing a secret.

Super! Time for another silver shield, don't you think?

Apprentice Wizard Challenge 2

Challenge 1
Can you pick words from the cauldron that rhyme with the words below and share the same letter strings?

a pear _____ _____ _____

b real _____ _____ _____

c bait _____ _____ _____

d book _____ _____ _____

e boot _____ _____ _____

f ear _____ _____ _____

g peer _____ _____ _____

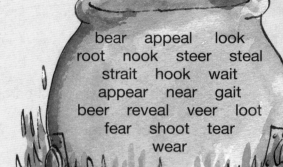

bear appeal look
root nook steer steal
strait hook wait
appear near gait
beer reveal veer loot
fear shoot tear
wear

Challenge 2
Can you write in the missing possessive pronouns in these sentences?

a Miss Snufflebeam played with _____ magic crystals.

b Mugly and Bugly argued about _____ food.

c Wizard Whimstaff practised _____ new spells.

d Miss Snufflebeam pointed out which bag was _____.

e The spider scuttled back to _____ web.

f "That's _____!" said Mugly and Bugly, grabbing the last piece of cake.

g "You can't have that, it's _____," said Miss Snufflebeam.

h The owls flew back to _____ nest.

i "If you can't find your wand, you can borrow _____," said Wizard Whimstaff.

Challenge 3
Can you find the 10 onomatopoeic words hidden in the puzzle grid?

c	r	a	s	h	p	s
r	i	p	w	h	a	n	s	m
u	p	l	o	p	n	a	c
n	i	p	o	p	s	c	k
c	n	l	b	o	l	k
h	g	z	h	i	s	s

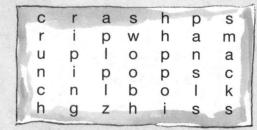

crash   smack
crunch   snap
rip   wham
plop   ping
pop   hiss

Challenge 4

Can you use your magical rules for suffixes to complete these word sums?

a   cope + ing = _____

b   wake + ing = _____

c   care + free = _____

d   empty + ness = _____

e   carry + er = _____

f   hope + less = _____

g   shape + ly = _____

h   pave + ed = _____

i   hungry + ly = _____

j   shady + est = _____

Challenge 5

Imagine you are being sent to take notes at the launch of a new type of flying broomstick and will have to write a newspaper report later. Using **when**, **where**, **why**, **what** and **who**, write a list of the questions you would ask on a separate sheet of paper.

Challenge 6

Can you finish these line poems? You need to remember things you saw and heard in each season.

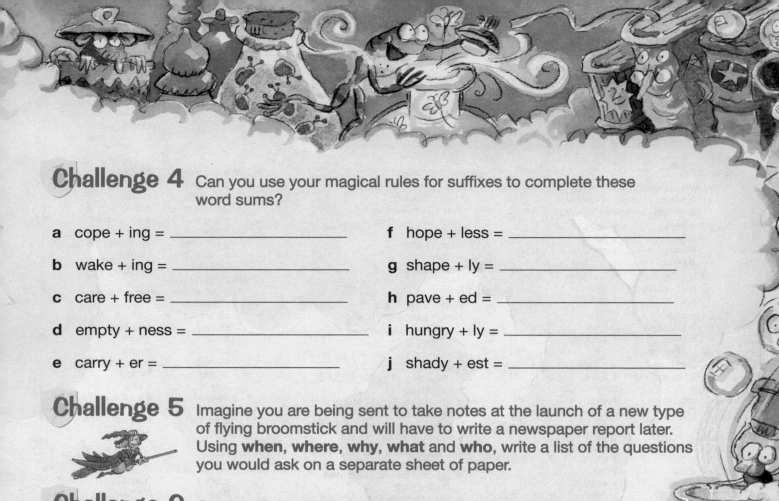

a   Winter is dark afternoons
    Frost crunching underfoot
    Christmas coming
    Warm woolly scarves

b   Spring is first greens appearing
    Yellow trumpets
    Short, sharp showers
    Misty mornings

6

5

4

3

2

1

Challenge Score

Count how many challenges you got right and put stars on the test tube to show your score. Then take the last silver shield for your trophy!

Answers

Pages 2–3

Task 1 Words ending in -es in the plural are:
b hexes; **d** boxes; **e** benches;
g wishes; **h** hisses; **i** witches

Task 2 **a** toys   **e** keys
b trays   **f** parties
c jellies   **g** puppies
d cries   **h** worries

Task 3 **a** salmon   **d** scissors
b spectacles   **e** shorts
c deer   **f** buffalo

Task 4 **a** mice   **d** women
b children   **e** dice
c men   **f** people

Sorcerer's Skill Check
a babies   **e** dishes
b houses   **f** lollies
c girls   **g** mackerel
d buses   **h** women

Pages 4–5

Task 1 **a** broccoli   **g** emu
b kiwi   **h** comma
c polka   **i** pizza
d sofa   **j** cello
e igloo   **k** potato
f tango   **l** piano

Task 2 **-s words**
radios, solos, zoos, pianos
-es words
volcanoes, echoes, cargoes,
dominoes

Task 3 **a** skis   **e** patios
b saunas   **f** tattoos
c fungi   **g** sheep
d yo-yos   **h** spaghetti

Task 4 **a** bananas   **f** pizzas
b mangoes   **g** bhajis
c ice creams   **h** potatoes
d tomatoes   **i** beef
e broccoli   **j** fish

Sorcerer's Skill Check
The correct spellings are:
a umbrellas
b superheroes
c cameras
d ravioli
e discos

Pages 6–7

Task 1 **happy**   **hot**   **clothing**
blissful   warm   togs
joyful   scalding   garments
contented   boiling   outfit
delighted   roasting   uniform

Task 2 **a** angry   **d** puff
b quickly   **e** gobbled
c row   **f** seized

Task 3 Many answers are possible.

Task 4 Many answers are possible.

Sorcerer's Skill Check
The pairs are as follows:
magic, sorcery
bewitched, spellbound
magician, conjurer
happy, glad
cave, grotto
creepy, spooky
swamp, bog

Pages 8–9

Task 1 Direct speech: **a, b, d**
Reported speech: **c, e, f**

Task 2 **a** Wizard Whimstaff said, "Let's clean
up the cave."
b Pointy asked, "Where are Mugly
and Bugly?"
c "Time to go!" called out Miss
Snufflebeam.
d "Grub's up!" yelled Mugly and
Bugly.
e Miss Snufflebeam said, "This is
very confusing!"

Task 3 Correct answers may vary slightly
from the following:
a "It's time for tea," said Miss
Snufflebeam.
b "Can we have a snack?" asked
Mugly and Bugly.
c "You should try the new spell,"
Wizard Whimstaff told Pointy.

Task 4 Correct answers may vary slightly
from the following:
a Pointy complained that he was
cold.
b Wizard Whimstaff asked where his
crystal ball was.
c Miss Snufflebeam said the spell
was tricky.

Sorcerer's Skill Check
Many answers are possible.

Pages 10–11

Task 1 Many answers are possible.

Task 2 **a** trots happily; giggles; is cheerful
b is grumpy; grumbles angrily;
complains loudly
c thrashes wildly; is huge; roars
furiously

Task 3 Many answers are possible.

Task 4 Many answers are possible.

Sorcerer's Skill Check
Many answers are possible.

Pages 12–13

Task 1 **a** thankful
b merciful
c shameful
d dreadful
e playful
f fanciful
g scornful
h plentiful

Task 2 These words start with a soft c:
celery, circle, centre, cereal, cycle,
cinema.
ce, ci and cy usually softens the c.

Task 3 **a** beeping   beeper
b digging   digger
c running   runner
d training   trainer
e swimming   swimmer
f fitter   fitted
g dreamer   dreamed
h player   played
i helper   helped

Sorcerer's Skill Check
The following words are spelt
incorrectly:
incorrect   **correct**
stoped   stopped
sircus   circus
suny   sunny
colourfull   colourful
sycled   cycled
funy   funny
beautyful   beautiful
huming   humming
cheerfull   cheerful
hapy   happy

Pages 14–15

Challenge 1
a bingo   **g** panda
b pasta   **h** magnolia
c ski   **i** salsa
d eskimo   **j** hello
e camera   **k** area
f pogo

Challenge 2
Singular   **Plural**
dog   dogs
dish   dishes
box   boxes
loss   losses
lady   ladies
baby   babies

Challenge 3
Many answers are possible.

Challenge 4
Correct answers may vary slightly
from the following.
a "I'm going for a walk," said Wizard
Whimstaff.
b "Where's the potion, Pointy?"
asked Miss Snufflebeam.
c "We're hungry!" said Mugly and
Bugly.
d "The spell has worked," Pointy told
Wizard Whimstaff.

Challenge 5
Introduction, build-up, conflict,
climax, resolution

Challenge 6
a bashful   **b** grateful
c circle   **d** cycle

Pages 16–17

Task 1 **a** The two sound groups are as
follows:
Beard, fear, year, near, hear, should
be coloured in blue.
Search, earth, yearn, heard, should
be coloured in red.
b The two sound groups are as
follows:
Piece, niece, field, yield, grieve,
should be coloured in blue.
Tie, fried, lied, tried, should be
coloured in red.

Task 2 a eight, freight.
The **e** before the letter string affects its sound.
b earn, yearn.
The **n** following the letter string affects its sound.
c look, rook.
The **k** following the letter string affects its sound.

Task 3 a our   **b** ight
c ear   **d** ie

Task 4 a right, tight   **e** favour, flavour
b fear, year   **f** pour, your
c wear, bear   **g** soot, foot
d niece, piece   **h** bare, scare

Sorcerer's Skill Check
Many answers are possible.

Pages 18–19

Task 1 a my   mine
b your   yours
c his   his
d her   hers
e its   its

Task 2 a its   **d** his
b Her   **e** mine
c their

Task 3 a his   **d** its
b their   **e** their
c yours   **f** ours

Task 4 Many answers are possible.

Sorcerer's Skill Check
Hidden character is Wizard Whimstaff. For your own description, many answers are possible.

Pages 20–21

Task 1 crash, pop, fizz, clang, drip, whoosh

Task 2 crunch, screech, crackle, crinkle, hiss

Task 3 a bubbled   **d** trickled
b bang   **e** ding dong
c munched

Task 4 Many answers are possible.

Sorcerer's Skill Check
Many answers are possible.

Pages 22–23

Task 1 a leaping   **d** hoping
b baking   **e** teaching
c breaking   **f** taming

Task 2 a tuneful   **e** lively
b careless   **f** saved
c blameworthy   **g** nicest
d notable   **h** bravely

Task 3 a happiness   happier
b loveliness   lovelier
c heaviness   heavier
d creepiness   creepier
e emptiness   emptier
f carrying   carried
g trying   tried
h replying   replied
i drying   dried
j denying   denied

Sorcerer's Skill Check
a shyly   **d** brainiest
b greedily   **e** fried
c scurried

Pages 24–25

Task 1 Many answers are possible.

Task 2 a The new growing spell shrank the leader of the Magic Circle.
b At the Wizard's convention.
c Because one of the ingredients was missing.
d The leader of the Magic Circle.
e Last Tuesday.

Task 3 The following sentences wouldn't work:
a It was sort of dark, really.
b The Wizard's convention will be held last week. It's a great success.
c The troll denies stealing the wand, but he probably did.
d The flood swept through the town. "Everything was soaked." The rain finally stopped on Thursday.

Task 4 Many answers are possible.

Sorcerer's Skill Check
Many answers are possible.

Pages 26–27

Task 1 Green is a **juicy** apple
The **rolling** hills
A **munching** caterpillar
A **crispy** lettuce
A **hopping** frog
A **sparkling** emerald
The **first** leaf of spring
And a **well-clipped** lawn.
Green is the colour of nature.

Task 2 The following lines belong to the poem:
swelling puddles
drumming on umbrellas
gushing in gutters
rattling on the roof
soaking the roots of plants

Task 3 Many answers are possible.

Task 4 Many answers are possible.

Sorcerer's Skill Check
a Friendship is sharing a secret.
b Blue is a summer sky.
c Autumn is russet leaves rustling.
d Foods I love are chocolate and cake.
e Seaside holidays are buckets and spades.
f A trip to the zoo means zebra stripes.

Pages 28–29

Challenge 1
a bear   wear   tear
b appeal   reveal   steal
c strait   gait   wait
d hook   look   nook
e root   shoot   loot
f fear   appear   near
g steer   veer   beer

Challenge 2
a her   **f** ours
b their   **g** mine
c his   **h** their
d hers   **i** mine
e its

Challenge 3

Challenge 4
a coping
b waking
c carefree
d emptiness
e carrier
f hopeless
g shapely
h paved
i hungrily
j shadiest

Challenge 5
Many answers are possible.

Challenge 6
Many answers are possible.

The end

Wizard's Trophy of Excellence

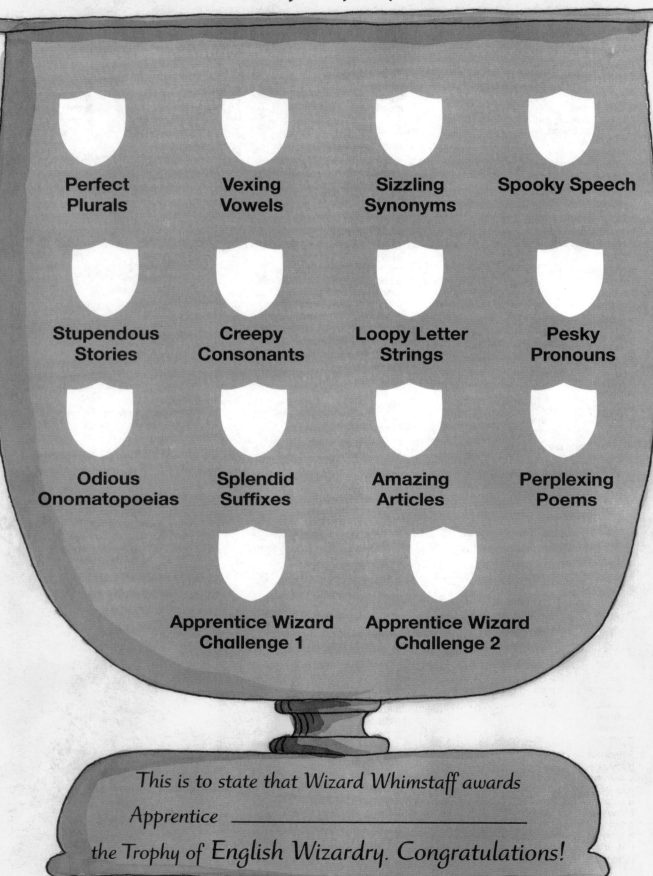

Perfect Plurals

Vexing Vowels

Sizzling Synonyms

Spooky Speech

Stupendous Stories

Creepy Consonants

Loopy Letter Strings

Pesky Pronouns

Odious Onomatopoeias

Splendid Suffixes

Amazing Articles

Perplexing Poems

Apprentice Wizard Challenge 1

Apprentice Wizard Challenge 2

This is to state that Wizard Whimstaff awards

Apprentice _____

the Trophy of English Wizardry. Congratulations!